# Block Town
## Learning Simple Patterns

by Lynn Maslen Kertell
pictures by Sue Hendra and John R. Maslen

Scholastic Inc.
New York • Toronto • London • Auckland • Sydney • Mexico City • New Delhi • Hong Kong • Buenos Aires

Seth and Mac were building
a block town.

Block by block the town grew.
The blocks made a pattern.

Seth's friends wanted to help build the block town.

Sally and Tanner put blocks down, but the blocks didn't fit the pattern.

"Try another way," Seth suggested.

Sally and Tanner pushed
the blocks aside.

Sally and Tanner looked at the
scattered blocks. They did not give up.

They turned the blocks upside down,
around and over. They kept on trying.

Seth had an idea. Together the
four friends looked at the shapes.

"Square, rectangle, rectangle!"
they said. "Now we can build."

Adding to the pattern, Sally, Tanner, and Seth built a fantastic block town.